For Clare, Anna, and Simon

Oxford University Press, Great Clarendon Street, Oxford OX2 6DP

Oxford New York
Athens Auckland Bangkok Bogota Bombay
Buenos Aires Calcutta Cape Town Dar es Salaam
Delhi Florence Hong Kong Istanbul Karachi
Kuala Lumpur Madras Madrid Melbourne
Mexico City Nairobi Paris Singapore
Taipei Tokyo Toronto Warsaw

and associated companies in
Berlin Ibadan

Oxford is a trade mark of Oxford University Press

Copyright © Brian and Rebecca Wildsmith 1994
First published 1994
First published in paperback 1997
Reprinted 1997

A CIP catalogue record for this book is available from the
British Library

ISBN 0 19 272313 8

Printed in Hong Kong

Jack
and the
Meanstalk

Brian and Rebecca Wildsmith

OXFORD UNIVERSITY PRESS

Professor Jack was a scientist. He loved to eat fresh
vegetables, so he grew them in his garden.
One day he decided that his vegetables weren't growing fast
enough.
'I will have to invent something to hurry them up,' he said.

Early next morning, Professor Jack heard a loud crash. His experiment had worked so well that one of the plants had gone right through the roof.

The villagers, the fire brigade, and two television crews all arrived to see the amazing plant.

The plant went on growing and growing. It soared
high up into the sky, until it was almost out of sight.

The plant grew so high that it burst through the ozone
layer, and its thousands of leaves blocked out the sunlight.
Fighter planes tried to shoot it down, but still it grew.

The roots grew so deep into the earth, that they
crashed through the countryside, destroying towns,
villages, and anything in their way.

Things got even worse. Satellite pictures showed a giant space monster climbing down towards Planet Earth. People were terrified. No one knew what to do.

The animals decided that something had to be done.
Very soon they would have nowhere to live and nothing
to eat or drink. So they called an emergency meeting.

'What can we do?' asked the rabbits.
'We must get to the root of the problem,' said Fox.
'That's it!' said Owl. 'The roots! We must eat through
the roots of this plant and kill it once and for all.'

Foxes, rabbits, moles – anyone who could burrow – waited
for Owl's command. Then they started to dig and gnaw and
bite through the roots of the giant plant.

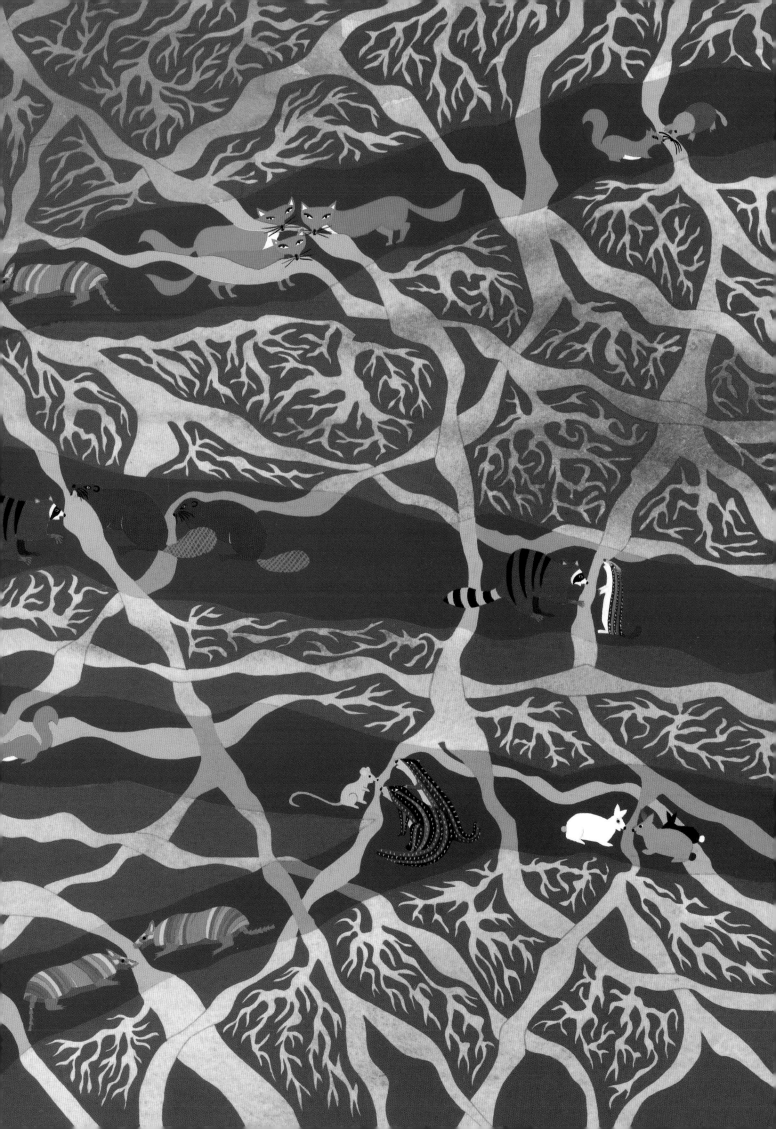

Day after day the animals tore at the plant with their teeth and their claws. Night after night, the giant space monster climbed down the leaves. Slowly the plant grew weaker and weaker, until at last it died. It snapped into pieces and fell into space, taking the monster with it.

It was a long time before the countryside recovered,
and the towns and villages were rebuilt.
Professor Jack mended his house and started growing
vegetables again. Only this time, he didn't do any
experiments. He let nature do the work all by itself.
And it did.